Introductory Digital Logic Lab
A Graphical Approach to Logic Design

MW01089742

By
Captain Tim Johnson, PE
Associate Professor
Department of Electronics and Mechanical
Wentworth Institute of Technology
550 Huntington Ave.
Boston, Massachusetts, 02115
johnsont@wit.edu

Andrew Tracy
Wentworth Institute of Technology
550 Huntington Ave.
Boston, Massachusetts, 02115
tracya@wit.edu

First Printing: April, 2007 by Lightning Source, Inc.

Other Books by Tim Johnson
> *Finding a Job in Tough Times, 2002*
> *History of Open-Water Marathon Swimming, 2004*
> *Stud of the Hudson, A Swim in Twenty Stages, 2006*
> *The History of Open-Water Marathon Swimming, Color Edition 2007*
> *Performance Sailing on a J29, 2007*

Cover photo by Capt. Tim Johnson, PE

The author extends his thanks to Andrew Tracy for his leadership in writing some of the crucial labs for this book. Without his help, insight, and willingness to work with the author this lab book would not have come into existence. Thanks are also extended to Joe Diecidue of Wentworth Institute of Technology for his assistance with the technical procedures for setting up the Agilent oscilloscope to capture sample waveforms of switch bounce.

Publisher:
Captain's Engineering Services
Buzzards Bay, MA 02532
(www.captainsengsvc.com)

ISBN 0-9721726-4-5

Rationale

Why another book on logic circuits when there are so many that address the subject so well? The book was written with the novice in mind whose first day on the job will find him so far behind industry practices that the connection between the classroom and the theory bears little resemblance with the practice. With a classical breadboard approach to learning logic, the student is so poorly prepared for the experience of logic design as it is practiced in industry that they will think their education has been wasted. Their effort to get up to speed will result in poor job evaluations and only the most adapt will survive, possibly by transferring to other departments. Undergraduate students should be able to walk out of college ready to undertake upgrading of a company's intellectual property to the latest interface in a week's time and not after a six-month learning curve.

This lab book takes the Altera software Quartus II and their design principles to guide the student through the basic steps of logic design without bogging them down in Boolean Theorems or VHDL structure. By separating the classical theory and the software from learning VHDL language, the student's tasks in mastering digital logic are lessened. By using the Quartus II graphical interface the student's success in understanding more complicated design work becomes an intuitive extension of their learning seeing that the implementation of a logic design is a given with the Quartus II software and not a laborious exercise to construct and debug physical circuits constructed of antiquated parts. This approach by Altera and others to logic design has succeeded in industry to the extent that when a new product hits the store shelves, complete changes to similar devices occur in a matter of months. Just look at how fast USB became accepted and then commonplace. Learning the techniques to logic design should be just as quick.

These labs introduce students to Altera's Quartus II Software. Students work in a design environment used for system-on-a-programmable-chip (SOPC). Logic circuit can be modeled graphically, simulated, then programmed into a chip for real world testing. Students learn the basics of design flow consisting of: Design Entry, Synthesis, Place and Routing, Simulation, Timing Analysis, JTAG programming, and Configuration. These are taught by examples clearly pointing out the steps one takes in each phase of the design. It is imperative that the students observe their design work on an evaluation board. Since the UP-1Evaluation board was the first available this book was written with that configuration in mind. Later evaluation boards will be incorporated as they are adopted in greater numbers. The chip that is on the Altera UP-1 evaluation boards is the EPM7128SLC84-7. This chip has 84 pins and operates at 25 MHz in this application. Quartus II is the type of design software that industry uses today. These labs prepare students to use the methodology of today's logic design professionals. In these introductory labs, no VHDL programming knowledge is needed or used leaving the students free to concentrate on the logic in their circuit designs.

The number of labs presented is kept below the normal amount that a 3-credit introductory college course may offer so that the professor can substitute in their favorite labs and make sure that the basic principles of breadboards (inputs, outputs, power and ground) are taught and understood. After about the fourth week of logic circuits, the students should become acquainted with the software techniques that will allow them to implement in minutes what previously would take two or three labs session to accomplish.

The author would appreciate comments, concerns, and suggestions to help improve the subjects addressed in introductory classes. The labs offered have all been field tested by students at the college where the author teaches and their comments were invaluable. As the students became more proficient in the software, less and less assistance by way of step-by-step instruction was given. A learning process is assumed with later labs incorporating prior learning. None of the classical theory was abandon in the lectures but the emphasis was on how these ideas are implemented in an application.

Index

Introduction to Quartus

Preliminaries

1. Download the software onto you computer
   a. Visit www.altera.com.
   b. Click on Design Software found under Products.
   c. This screen shows various tools available for the digital designer. Find Quartus II Web Edition listed along the side bar and click on it.
   d. Start the download process by clicking on the free copy offered at the bottom of the page.
   e. In the first Table on this page, click on Quartus II Web Edition Software v6.0 Service Pack 1 which will take you to their License information page.
   f. Run the Quartus II execute file which installs the Quartus software in its own folder.
2. Obtain a license for the software.
   a. Your software will not run until a license file is installed on your computer. When you receive the license via email, put it where you can find it.
   b. Run the Quartus II software and on the interrupt screen that pops up immediately, click on the "..." so you can browse to the location of the license file.

Design Entry—Project

3. Open the software and begin the design entry by clicking on File from the main menu then clicking on New Project Wizard. Once a project is established you can reopen saved designs with Open Project.

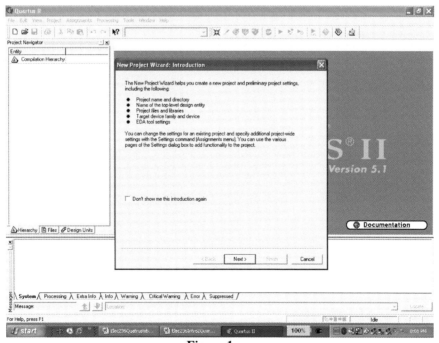

Figure 1

a. After clicking thru the first page of the Wizard, on the second page you MUST name the project. The project name and the top-level design are the same...automatically. I'd suggest MyFirstDesign.

b. Modify the default location for the working directory by adding a backslash with the project name you've chosen. Add a folder to the directory path by adding: /Projects/MyFirstDesign. Your screen should look like Figure 2. Click Next.

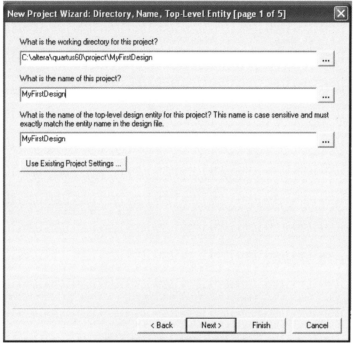

Figure 2 Naming the project

c. The next page allows you to add design files to a new project. Right now you have no design files to add because you haven't designed anything. Click on Next.

d. This page counts. Here you declare the chip that your design will be implement in. In the design flow this is called Synthesis. Change the Family from Stratix to MAX7000S. Now slide down the list of available chips in this family until you locate: EPM7128SLC84-7. This is the chip that is on-board the Altera UP-1 evaluation boards used here at Wentworth. This chip has 84 pins and operates at 25 Mhz. At this point you can now click Finish. Agreed to accept the creation of a new directory.

Figure 3

e. Notice how in the Project Navigator, when the Hierarchy tab is selected, the Entity lists the chip and under it is the name of our project. Double click on the project name. Quartus tells us that there is no design entity by that name to be found. This is our next phase of the design flow.

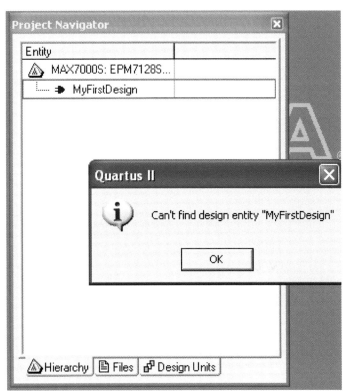

Figure 4 Project Navigator

Design Entry—Graphical Design Entity

4. In this phase, you enter the design using a graphical interface, similar to Pspice. Click on File again then New. In the text box that opens highlight Block Diagram/Schematic File then click OK.

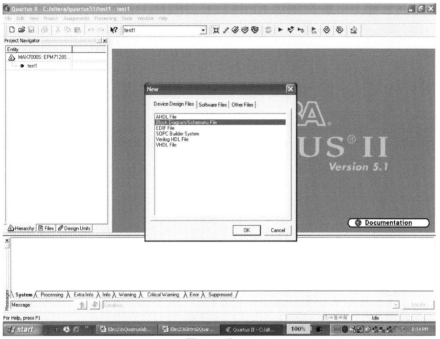

Figure 5

Figure 6 shows the working window, a virtual breadboard opens that is very similar to Pspice only much more powerful. Across the top of the window, a tab appeared with the default name of your design: Block1.bdf.

7

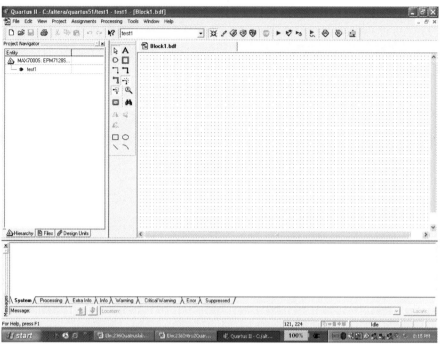

Figure 6

5. Down the middle partition are some of your graphical tools. First click on the breadboard. In order to add a part, Quartus needs to know where first. Now click on what looks like a two-input AND gate. The symbol library opens. This is your entry into the intellectual property world of Altera. Click on the plus symbol to open up the library, then on maxplus2 and slide down to check out what's available. Now click on the down arrow. Up pops a MUX chip. We'll get to what that chip does in another course. Continue pressing down until the 7408 chip is seen as in Figure 7.

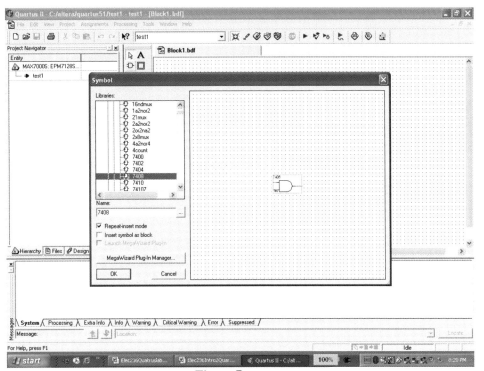

Figure 7

6. Click OK or left click the drawing and the chip is place on your virtual breadboard, move the cursor and click escape to stop placing duplicates of 7408. Left click on the highlighted design to see what is inside this block. Whoa, that looks like your design last week doesn't it? The title block shows that this was originally design in 1999. You'll never have to design another one. Click on the AND2 that is at the core of this design and the symbol properties will pop up. Click on Ports and you'll see that there are two input ports and one output port. Tell the box OK then click on the tab for this open design and Close the window.

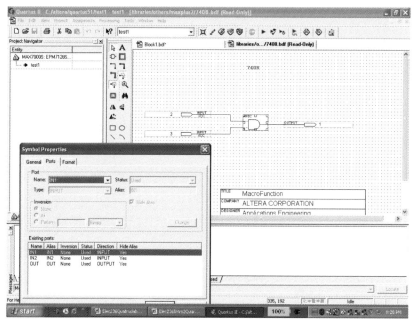

Figure 8

7. Let close the Library for Maxplus2 open primitives and logic. Slide down to add a 2-input OR gate called "or2". Left click on it to see its design. Surprised? There is no design, that's why they call them primitives; but there is the Symbol Properties. Click on Ports and it very similar to the AND gate. Click OK.

8. Let's connect these devices. If it was a real breadboard you'd use a wire. In Quartus there are a variety of wires to use as seen on the tool palate. The one we want is located right underneath the library icon. It's called an orthogonal node tool, fancy name for a wire. Click on it and the cursor will now connects ports. Connect the output of the AND to one of the inputs of the OR gate. Nothing fancy but we are working on a basic circuit equation (A·B)+C = Z. Position the cursor over the output of the AND. Hold down the left button and then move the cursor horizontally toward one of the input pins. If they don't align exactly move the cursor vertically. The wire only allow one 90 degree turn in it. If another turn is needed release the cursor and start another segment at the end of the last segment.

10

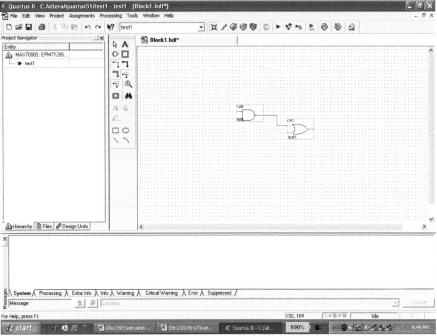

Figure 9

9. We'll need inputs and outputs next. We can find them in the Library. Under Primitives, expand "pins" and highlight the input pin. We'll need three of them; two on the inputs of the AND gate and one on the input of the OR gate. Oh, how do you tell the difference between inputs and outputs in these types of designs? Inputs are on the left, outputs on the right. Put an output pin on the output of the OR gate.

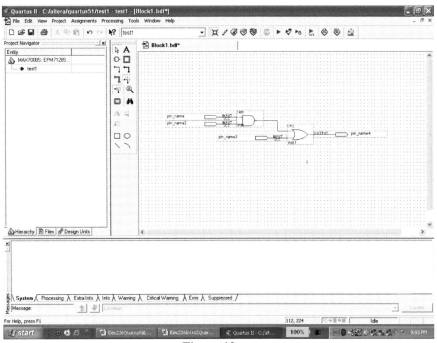

Figure 10

11

10. Your design should look something like Figure 10 above at this point. Let's name the pins. Double click on one of the pins, let's start at the upper left and rename it "A" using the Pin Properties. Name the other pins.

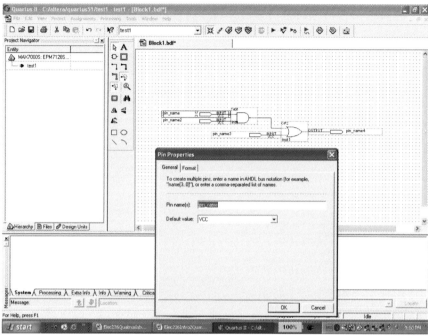

Figure 11

11. Now comes the hard part: the file has to be compiled. This is where we find out if there are any semantic errors and connection errors. In Quartus, it's always a wise decision to compile whenever you change or assign anything.

12. Start the compilation by clicking on the purple arrowhead next to the faded stop on the main menu bar. The progress of the compilation is shown in the Status box. When the compilation is complete, it will tell you how many errors you have. If there are, we've be notified and your job is to clear the errors. The software will highlight the errors in red in the message window along the bottom and if you double click on an error, the software will take you to the offending part or connection. You can ignore the warnings. Notice that it changed the name of the bdf file from Block1.bdf to test1.bdf. If you had save the file earlier as suggested to MyFirstDesign, the name of Block1 would have been changed to MyFirstDesign.

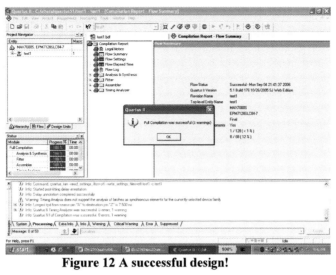

Figure 12 A successful design!

Synthesis

1. Synthesis is the evaluation of your design by the computer into digital applications. The first application is a simulator. We need to know that the design works correctly. Quartus has a Waveform Editor that writes a input file used by the simulator. We begin by opening the Waveform editor.

2. On the main menu, click on File then New. On the New text box, select the tab Other Files and then highlight Vector Waveform File.

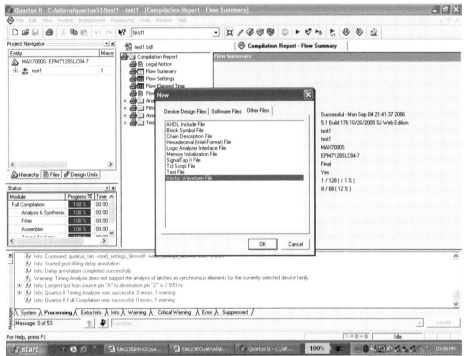

Figure 13

When you desktop looks like Figure 13, click OK.

15

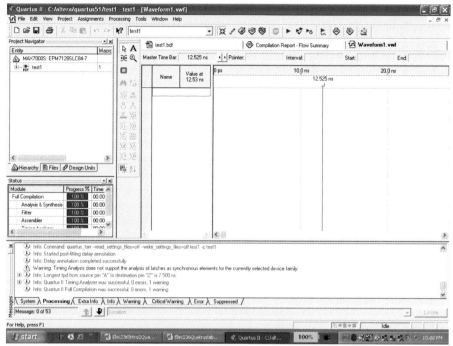

Figure 14 The Waveform Editor

3. With the Waveform Editor open, we need to insert nodes for timing. Just right click on the white space below Name on the waveform editor. This brings up the Insert Node or Bus text box seen in Figure 15.

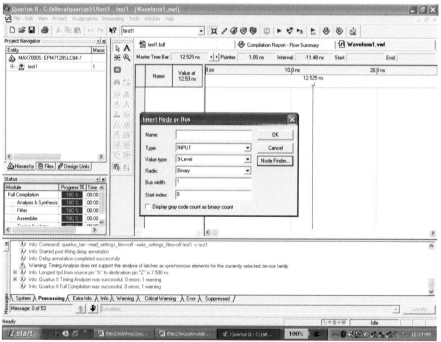

Figure 15

We're not done yet, click on the Node Finder button of this box.

16

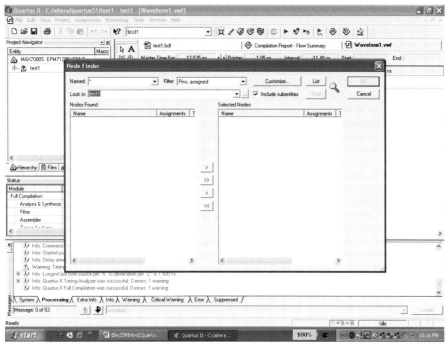

Figure 16

Still not done, Change the Filter to "Pins: all" then click on List up along the top of the Node Finder text box.

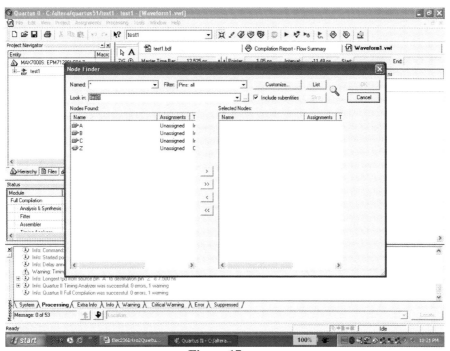

Figure 17

Finally, move only the nodes that you need to simulate the design onto the Selected Nodes side.

Figure 18

4. Click okay on the Node Finder (and the Insert Node or Bus) and the nodes now appear on the Waveform1.vwf under Name. All we have to do now is give the inputs some signal values.

5. Highlight the first input, right click, then click on value and select Clock (3rd from the bottom).

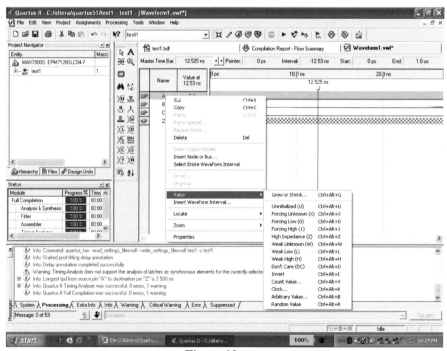

Figure 19

6. By clicking on Clock a new popup allows you to set the time period (frequency), insert an offset, and modify the duty cycle. These are handy attributes you'll want to play with when you do a Timing Analysis. Right now we just want to see if the design works so we set the parameters as described next.

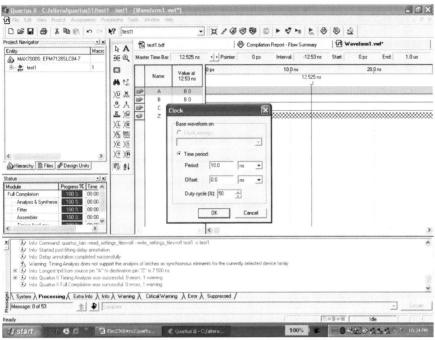

Figure 20

7. Make the time period 50 nanoseconds. Click OK. Notice that nothing changes on the display. That's because 25 nanoseconds is the first transition and that is all the window can see. Look for the zoom controls by going to the View menu off the main menu bar and zoom out.

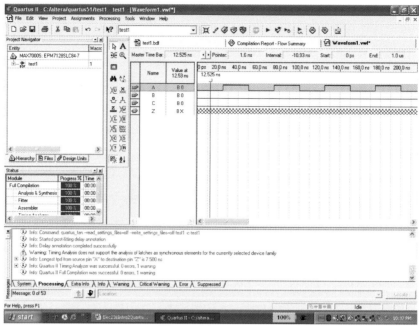

Figure 21

8. Set the other inputs at half the speed of the first and so on...(B = 100 nseconds, C=200 nseconds). Your waveform should look like Figure 22 at this point. We are just about ready to simulate the design where the indeterminate value (the XXX's) for Z are unassigned outputs values.

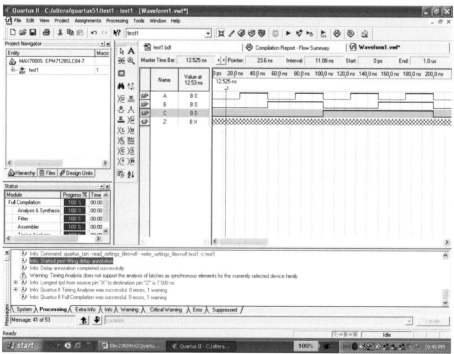

Figure 22

9. Before we can simulate the design we have to save the waveform file. Simple click on the waveform tab and close the window and the program will save the

file with our default design name. Since Z is an output, we don't need to assign it a signal. The output will be evaluated during simulation. It's not a bad idea to rename the file 3input.vwf as it can be reuse in any design having three inputs named A, B, and C.

10. Now we have to set this file as the input file for the Simulation.

11. Pull down Assignments on the main toolbar, click on Settings…a new window appears: Settings-test1. Along the navigation tree that appears along the left, click on Simulation.

12. In the window for Simulator Settings, the text box for Simulation input is set for test1.vwf. This is the correct file. If it wasn't, we could browse and identify the waveform for this design.

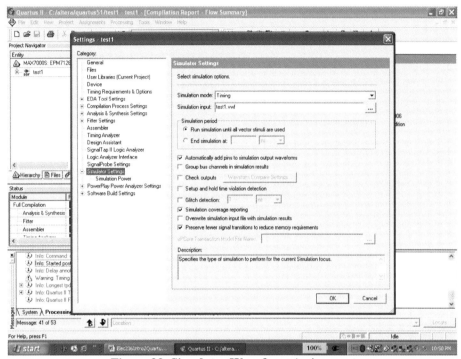

Figure 23 Simulator Waveform Assignment

13. Click Okay when you have the correct waveform file assigned as seen in Figure 23.

14. Now click on the Simulation icon off the main tool bar (blue arrow with a signal below it) and stand back as the computer is now going to do some work…

15. The output pin transitions will automatically be added. You may have to zoom out to see the full count.

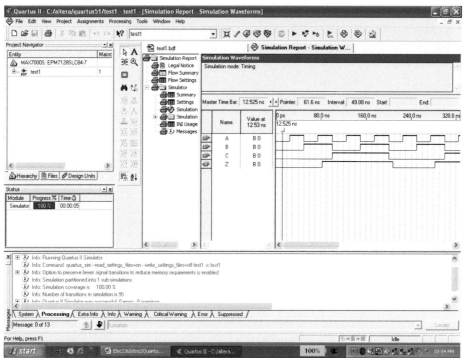

Figure 24 Simulation Output

16. Verify that the outputs change as desired. Don't let the machine think for you;
know and expect.

Place & Route

1. Since a programmable logic device can have innumerable design, the inputs and outputs tend to vary from design to design. For the EPM7128SLC84-7 the designer can set nearly anyone of its pins as input or output. In Place and Route we are assigning pins to specific inputs and outputs. Not all pins are available for assignment.

2. Bring your original design up by clicking on the test1.bdf tab in the work space. Click on Assignments along the main menu bar then select Pins to bring up the Assignment editor. It gets it own tab in the work space.

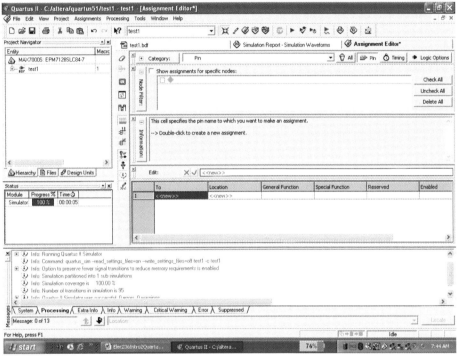

Figure 25 The Assignment Editor

3. Double click on the <<new>> in the To column near the bottom and take your pick of which pin to assign first. Now double click on <<new >> in the Location column and slide down to assign pin 34 to A. A new row appeared so complete the process assigning all the pins. Only assign pins label I/O for now.

23

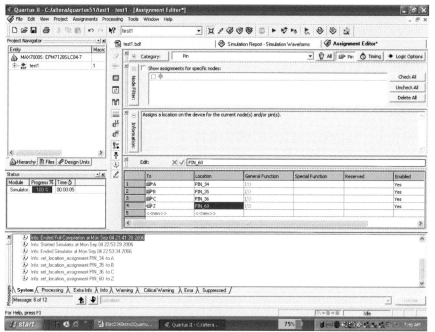

Figure 26

4. You could assign the pins sequentially or randomly, it doesn't matter for testing purposes. You can close the Assignment Editor tab for now. Sometimes on the UP-1 boards, we've re-assign the pins after testing because of defective I/O pins on the board. We're now ready for the next phase of downloading the program into the chip.

Programming & Configuration

1. Once pin assignments are set and the device selected, you can begin downloading your design to the board.
2. The first step with an IBM ThinkPad is to hook up the LPT1 port in the back of the computer to the input port of the UP-1. Use a male to female RS232 25-pin connector for the data. Plug in the UP-1 power transformer and a green LED lights.
3. Once the connection is confirmed between the computer and the UP-1 board, pull down on Tools off the main menu then click on Programming. The icon seen there is also in the main menu, second to last icon on the right. This opens the programming window for the test1.cdf file.

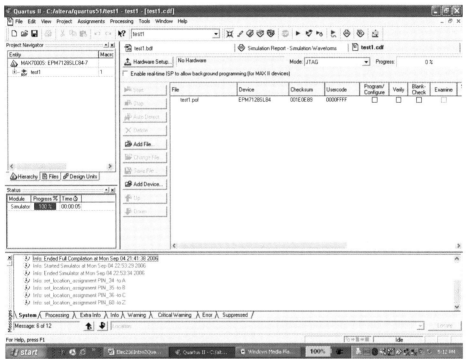

Figure 27 The Chip Programmer

4. Next click on the Hardware Setup button so that the text box opens and select ByteBlasterMV as the selected hardware. You may have to click on the Add Hardware button to finish the configuration. Also make sure the LPT1 port is selected. Your text box when the Add Hardware button closes should look like Figure 28.

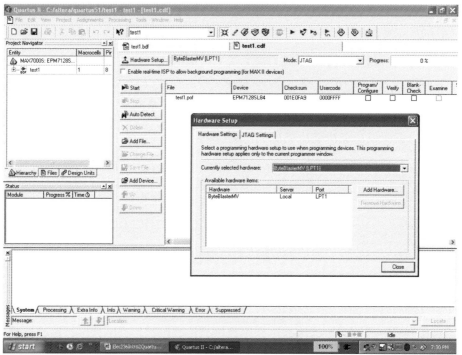

Figure 28 Hardware Setup

5. Close the Hardware Setup text box and then check off the Program/Configure box and the Verify box then click Start. The green LED next to the power LED will light up during the data download. When the process is complete the computer portion of the design is finished. Now we begin the Configuration phase.

6. Since there are a limited number of inputs and outputs plus the design is only a convenient educational example; the configuration is not complicated. Picked three toggle switches and wire them to the input pin locations. For the output, wire the output pin to one the LEDs present on the UP-1 evaluation board.

7. Does the LED light up when the simulation indicates (when Z=1)? Here's a quickie test....whenever C =1, Z is suppose to light up. Does it?

8. Test your toggle switch to make sure you are inputing a high when you throw the switch to make C high.

26

9. The problem may be because the LED are wired high. This means the LED light up when they are shown a ground. You are sending a high out on a true condition; there is no potential across the LED thus when C is high and Z is suppose to go high, you are turning off the LED. How could you solve this problem? We need to invert the output.

10. Go back to your original design and in the output path (before the output I/O pin) insert an inverter. They are also call NOT gates. Look in the Library under primitives/logic for the device.

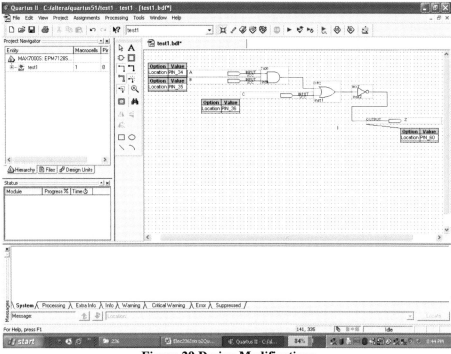

Figure 29 Design Modifications

11. Re-compile the design, don't brother with the simulation, drop this design into the chip and then test the output. Does it work properly? If so, print out a copy of the original design, the correct simulation, and have the instructor observe your working device on the evaluation board.

12. Except for the type of logic being implemented, this is the basic pattern for using Quartus software: open a project, open a type of design, place parts, compile (clear errors), make test waveform, simulate, declare pins, download to chip and verify. Good luck.

Using Block Symbols in Circuits

Objective: To familiarize the students with using logic gates in combination, their physical realization and Quartus block symbol design options.

Instructions:

1. Begin by opening a new project in Quartus. Name the project basic-combo-circuits. Notice that Quartus warns you about storing a different design in a folder that contains a design all ready (but it will permit it). Let's options not to stack designs in the same folder by adding "\basic-combo-circuits" to the working directory path in the first text field.

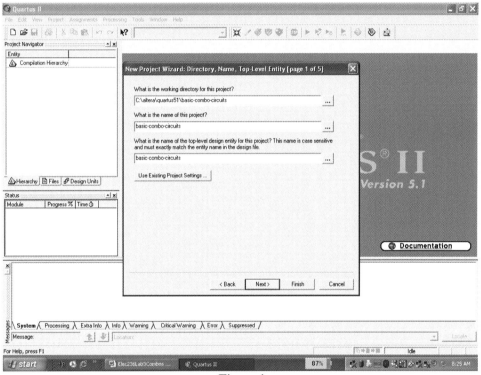

Figure 1

2. You can page thru the rest of the New Project Wizard if you like just to check that the setting for the device remain the same. We're not changing chips so leave everything the same as the first project.
3. Open a New Devise Design File (pull down on File off the main menu). Select Block Diagram/Schematic File.
4. Before we make a block symbol circuit, we'll first look at one. Open the library "...other/max2plus" and select 1a2nor2.

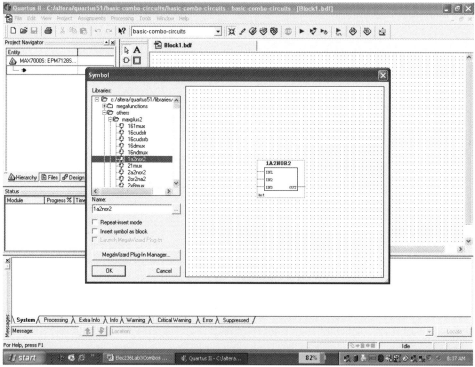

Figure 2

5. Right click on the device after you've dropped it into your design and select Open Design File.

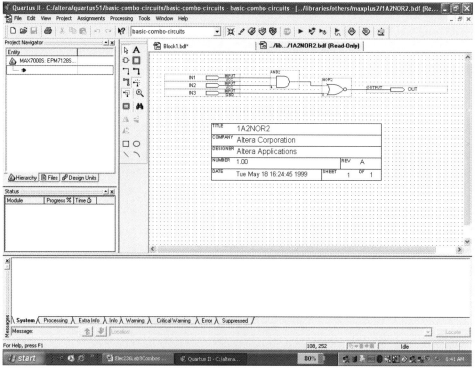

Figure 3

6. What is the Boolean equation for this design?

7. What is the truth table for this design?

8. Close the design file. Go back to the same library and select 2or2na2.

9. What is the Boolean equation for this design?

10. What is the truth table for this design?

11. Describe the naming convention for this library.

12. You are now going to design a 1or2na2 logic block (instructions follow); but first close the project we've been using without saving anything.

13. In order to find and use this symbol we'll need to add a folder to the library. From "My Computer" go to C:\altera\quartus51\libraries or C:\altera\quartus60\libraries depending on which version you are using. Once there, create a folder named "user defined". This folder is where we will place new block symbol files that we will create.

14. Begin making a block symbol by opening a new project and calling it 1or2na2.

15. Start by making a new schematic diagram for the logic of a 1or2na2. Save the file as 1or2na2 in the user defined folder we created. Compile your design; it never can hurt to compile your file whenever you finish a design, assign something, or change something. When in doubt: compile.

1. Second, create a new Block Symbol file by clicking File off the main menu, select New and then on the New text box clicking on the "other files" tab. Select Block Symbol file and click "OK".

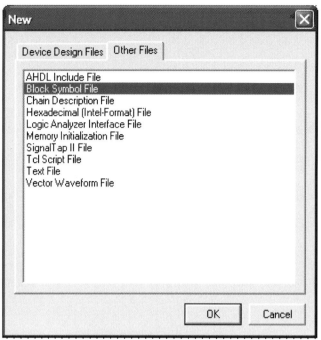

Figure 4 Selecting the file

2. A block called Symbol will appear in the file. The outer square in blue shows the work space for the symbol and then there is an inner square representing the logic contained therein. These areas are separated by a dashed light green boundary.

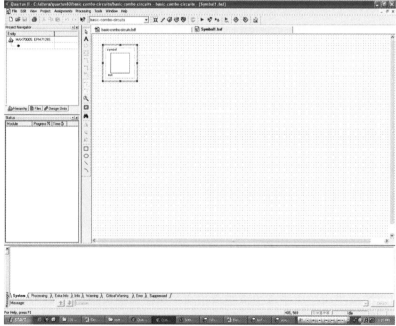

Figure 5 Basic block symbol

3. With the symbol selected, right click and open properties. Change the name of the symbol from "inst" to the same name as your design (it should be 1or2na2). Close this window.

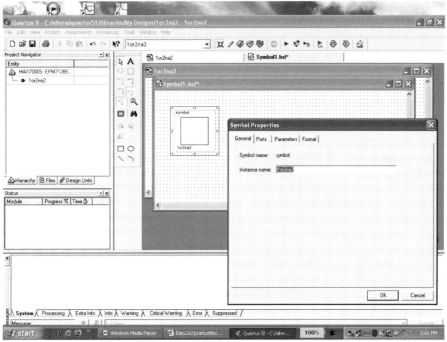

Figure 6

4. Now using File off the main menu save the project. *Save the block symbol with the same name as the schematic file*. The file extension for the symbol file is *.bsf while the actual design file is *.bdf. The BSF file extension can stand for Block Symbol File and BDF is Block Design File.

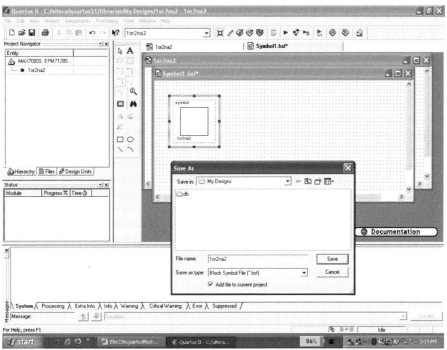

Figure 7

5. Now that the symbol is saved, right click on the symbol in the virtual breadboard and on the popup window select the *bdf file to associate with this symbol.   Up should pop the schematic design for this symbol (the OR and AND gate design).

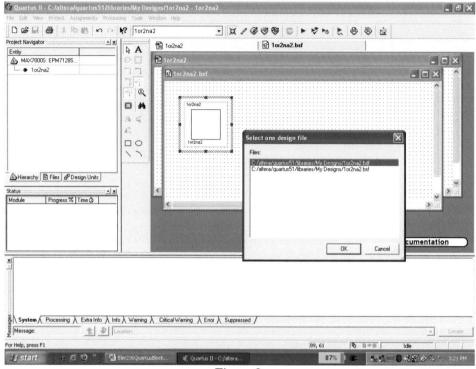

Figure 8

6. If the schematic file doesn't appear; there is an alternative method of associating this file with the symbol diagram: while the block symbol is select, pull down Project along the main menu, click on Add/Remove file in this project…then in this case remove the *.bsf file as seen in Figure 9.

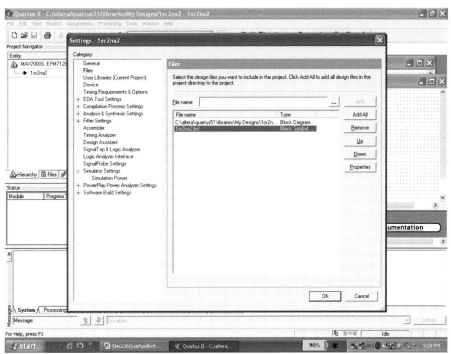

Figure 9

7. After this is finished, when you double click on the block diagram, the schematic will pop-up directly without having to choose between two different files.

8. Next, we create the connections of the 1or2na2 in the symbol diagram. You do this by clicking on the edge of the work space near the inner square block. Your cursor will change to a targeted bull's-eye when you pause between the outer boundary and a light green dashed line and a short horizontal line with an X at the end is to the lower right where the cursor arrow use to be. Double click the left cursor at this time and the Port text box opens. Enter the same name for each port as the schematic uses.

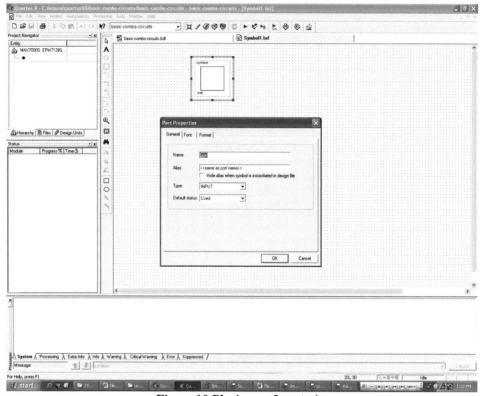

Figure 10 Placing an Input pin

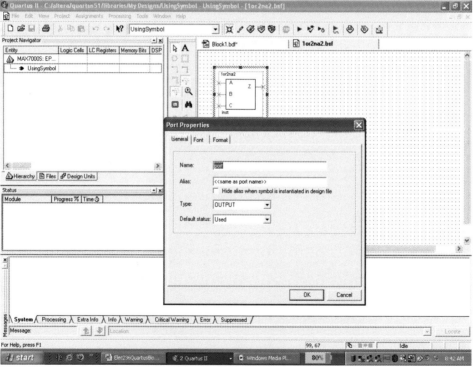

Figure 11 Output pin

9. It is good practice to put all the input pins on the left side, and all the output pins

on the right side. Note that the name of the pins in the block symbol **MUST** be the same as the pin names in the block diagram.

10. Repeat this process until you have all the needed pins.

11. Once finished, save/compile the file as "1or2na2" in the "user defined" folder we made. The block symbol file and the block design file (the schematic) are saved in the folder of the same name. You are finished making the Symbol containing your design. Next, we will use this symbol in another design.

12. Close out of everything and open a new project up; call it *basic-combo*. Pull down on File off the main menu, click on new, select Block Diagram/Schematic File to open up a blank virtual breadboard.

13. Using the 2or2na2, the 1or2nor2 and the 1or2na2, create the following circuit. Save it using the same name as the project.

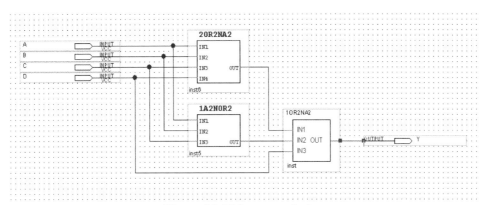

Figure 12 Using your design

23. Program your design in the UP-1 evaluation board, check the logic using the input toggle switches and route the output to an LED. Write down the observed logic table.

14. Now simulate the circuit. You'll need to create a 4-input waveform file which you should save as it can be reused. Record the results. Does your logic table match the results of the simulation?

15. For your lab report: turn in a copy of your symbol design (expanded), a copy of the design in which your symbol was used, a copy of those simulated results and answers to the various questions you encountered as you went thru this lab.

Parity Bit Generator

Objective: To create a parity bit generator used in data communication. The student will be introduced to the use of bus lines in a design and Count in the simulation.

Instructions:
1. Begin by crating a new project in Quartus called "ParityBitGenerator" saved in a folder of the same name in your project folder.
2. Next, create the following circuit.

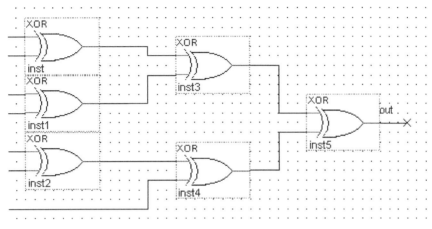

Figure 1

3. What is the Boolean equation of this circuit assuming inputs A thru G?

4. Is this an even or odd parity bit generator? Explain your answer.

5. Next, create one input pin named Input[6..0]. This will create a seven bit vector ranging from Input[0] to Input[6]. This is our new bus input for our circuit.

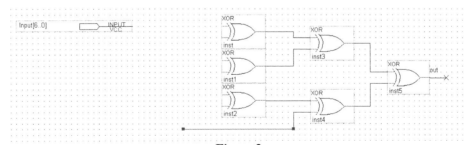

Figure 2

6. Next, create a bus line from the circuit using the bus tool found in the tool palette ⌐. You will notice that the bus line is wider then the normal lines that you have made up to this point.

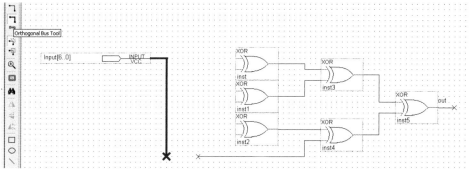

Figure 3

7. Next, connect node lines from the bus line to the seven inputs of the circuit. After connecting all of the node lines, right click each of them and go into its properties (Figure 4). There will be a field where you can name the node. Assign (name) each node connection Input (the same as the bus they connect to) but with a different input bit number. The bus ranges from Input[0] to Input[6]. Therefore you will need to name each of the nodes after a different bit on the bus: Input[0], Input[1], Input[2], ECT...

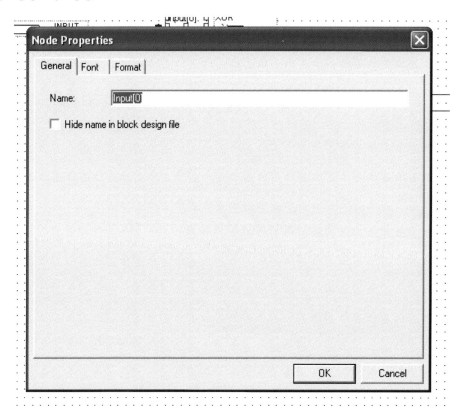

Figure 4 Node Properties

40

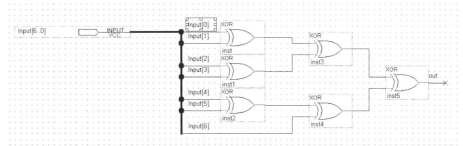

Figure 5

8. Continue to name all of the nodes from the bus until it represents Figure 5. Name the output node of the final XOR as "out" (this output is the parity bit).
9. Next is to create an output for the circuit. We already have an output for the parity bit, but this is useless on its own. The parity bit is only useful when it sent with the signal it was made for. Because of this, we will have to make an eight bit output bus to carry the value of "out" along with the seven bit input signal.
10. Create a new output pin and name it Output[7..0]. This will create an eight bit output. Connect a bus line to it (Figure 6)

Figure 6

11. We now name the bus line. A bus line can consist of multiple inputs or busses. To properly name the bus line we want to make the "out" value the MSB; therefore, we must name it first in the bus. The name of the bus will be "out, Input[6..0]" (Figure 7). This states that the MSB is the value of "out" and the other seven bits are the values of the input.

Figure 7

12. We now have our completed circuit (Figure 8). Notice that output[7..0] and its bus is not physically connected to the rest of the circuit. This is because a physically drawn connection is not needed as long as the nodes and busses are properly labeled.

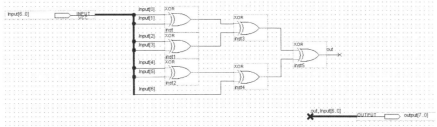

Figure 8

41

13. Now create a block symbol for the ParityBitGenerator. If you've forgotten the steps, review the procedure found in the Using Block Symbols in Circuits lab beginning with Step 16. Remember that the pin names of the block diagram and the block symbol must have the same name *and* the file names have to be the same. Save the *.bsf file in the folder you created for this design or in the User Defined folder under Libraries if you want the convenience option to reuse this design in other designs. The symbol will look like the block diagram seen in Figure 9. Input A and output X will both be busses.

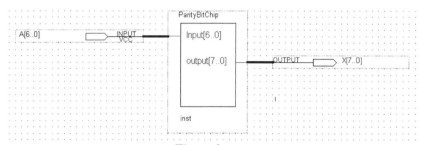

Figure 9

14. Now create a new waveform file. When using the node finder to add your inputs and outputs, you will notice that you will have a total of 17 options to chose from (Figure 10). This is because you could manipulate the entire bus at once in the waveform file, or could select individual nodes of that bus.

15. If you don't find all these pins, go to Project and check if you have all the files in the project. You may have to add the Paritybitchip.bdf. Save the file then compile the entire project.

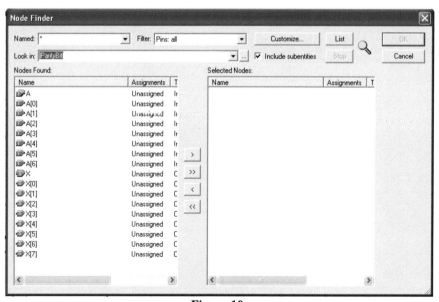

Figure 10

16. In Figure 10, the symbol next to both A and X looks like 3 pins stacked on top of each other. This is because they are both busses.

17. Add only A and X to the waveform file. Notice that in the waveform file both A and X have a plus sign next to it (Figure 11). This means they can be expanded by clicking on the plus sign.

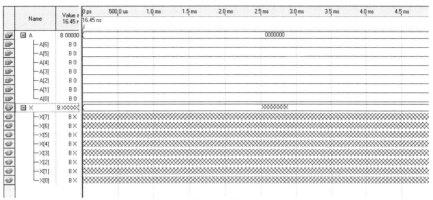

Figure 11

18. Select the A bus, right click to open up the options box, select Value, then select Count Value.

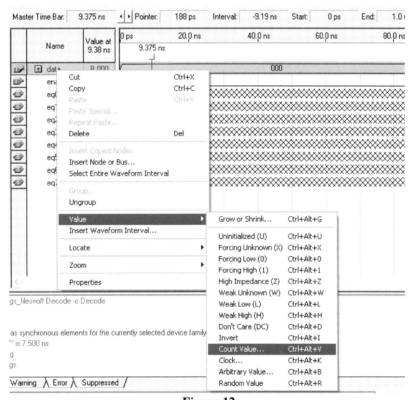

Figure 12

19. On the Count Value pop-up box, most of the setting in the Counting tab are okay (radix = binary) because the project was compiled; see Figure 13. I prefer the Timing to be slightly slower. So click on the Timing tab and change the *Count every* 10 ns to 20 ns then click okay. Notice that the period for the simulation lasts from 0 ps to 1 μsecond.

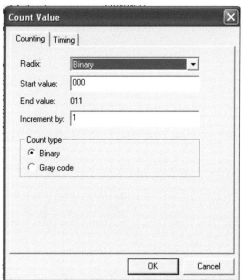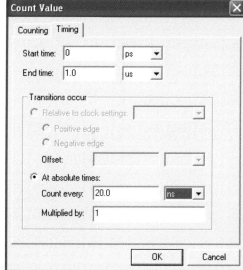

Figure 13

20. The upper time limit for the simulation can be change in the Count Value text box or by clicking on Edit in the main menu then selecting End Time. Set the upper limit for 2ms because a count with 2^6 combinations creates thousands of values. Simulate your circuit and print out your results.

21. After you assign pins to your design and recompile the design, download your program onto the UP1 board. Do your results from the board match those from the simulation?

22. Now modify your BitParityChip files to have a controller bit that will allow the user to change it between being an even or odd parity bit generator. (The controller bit should not be part of any of the busses).

23. Simulate your new design. After you've added a pin for the new input, recompile the design, and download the program to the UP-1 board to test the design.

24. You don't have to wire up all the outputs, only the parity bit is of interest. If you have not insert an inverter in the output of the parity bit, remember the following rule for inverse logic: LED on—Logic low; LED off—Logic High. Have your instructor look at your results. Print out all of your design files and the simulation.

Megafunctions

Objective: Students use the megafunction wizard to create a decoder circuit.

Instructions:
1. Open up a new project design called Decode in a directory called Decode. Once the project is established, use New to open a Block Diagram/Schematic File where we will work.

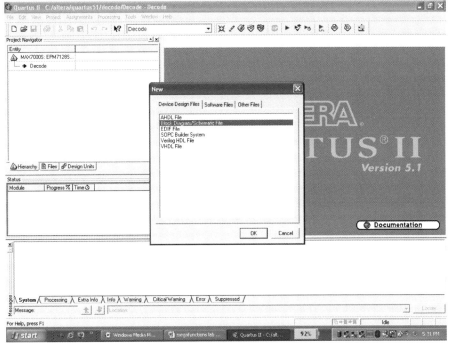

Figure 1

2. Once the virtual breadboard is open, click on the icon for access to the libraries (the Symbol Tool). Click on the MegaWizards Plug-In Manager in the lower left of the Symbol window as seen in Figure 2.

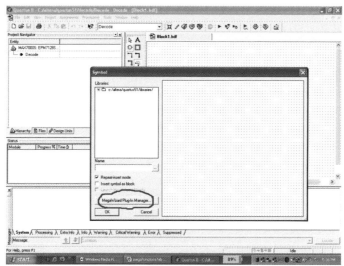

Figure 2

3. When page 1 of the MegaWizard Plug-In Manager opens, leave the default choice as is: Create a new custom megafunction variation. Click on Next.

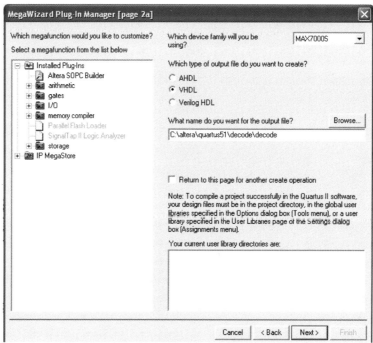

Figure 3

4. When page 2a opens, make sure the options, chip family, and output file look like the selections in Figure 3. VHDL is the Hardware Description Language that the file may use instead of graphical images. Note that you need to add the actual file name for this new design (the reason the word decode follows the designated folder). There is no need to check any of the other boxes for this design.

5. We are going to explore the various devices available in the default libraries. Open the various directories and take a peek at the available designs. When you

complete this lab you will be know the steps necessary to implement any of these designs. Some of these designs you will have the pleasure of revisiting in more advanced logic classes. When you finish browsing, highlight LPM_DECODE as seen in Figure 4. Click on Next

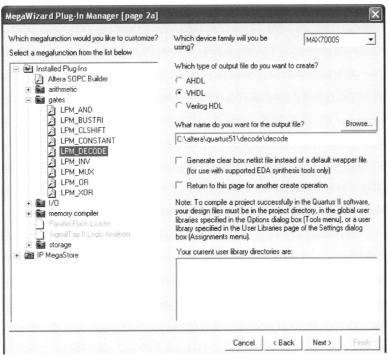

Figure 4

6. The LPM means library of parameterized modules. Some designs are so standardized that the inputs and output seldom vary between designs but those that do can be set as a parameter. For instance, the difference between an 8 bit input, a 16 bit input and a 32 bit input vary little except for the number of inputs. The number becomes a parameter of the design. All LPM designs allow designers to use a proven module that can be customized. Page 3 of the wizard begins this process. You go thru the various choices and set them to fit your design needs. Design options not selected are eliminated from the design.

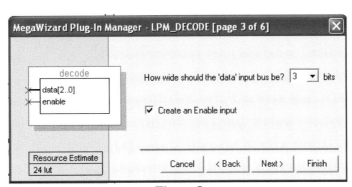

Figure 5

7. Let's make the data bus 3 bits wide and an Enable input as seen in Figure 5.

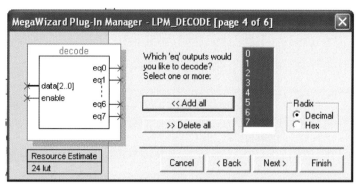

Figure 6

8. On page 4, let's go for broke and decode all 8 inputs variations (remember, in the digital world, zero counts). Click on <<Add all. Your wizard should look like Figure 6.

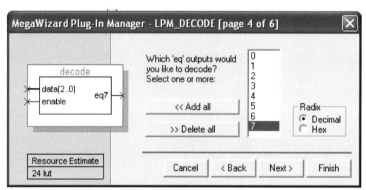

Figure 7

9. If we wanted, we could add just selected digital inputs as seen in Figure 7. You would do this if you were setting up a device to respond to a single code on a bus to possibly turn on the attached devise. For our purposes, include all the outputs as in Figure 6 and leave the Radix in decimal (chcck box on the right).

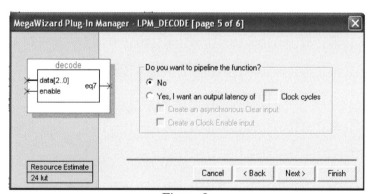

Figure 8

10. On page 5, decline the offer to pipeline…an architecture beyond the scope of this tutorial.

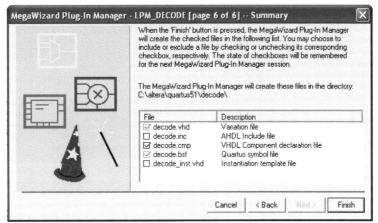

Figure 9

11. Page 6 of the wizards lets you review the files that will be created. Presently, we will be only using the Quartus symbol file: decode.bsf.

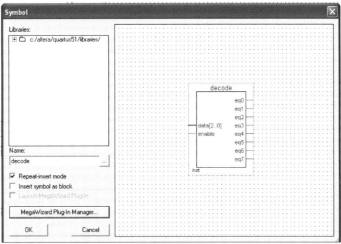

Figure 10

12. This is our custom megawizard function that we designed using the wizard. Paste it into your design by clicking okay.

13. Save the file (just in case...) at this point as decode_all (the *.bsf comes up automatically) as seen in Figure 10. Notice the box checked of that adds this file to the current project. That saves a step or two.

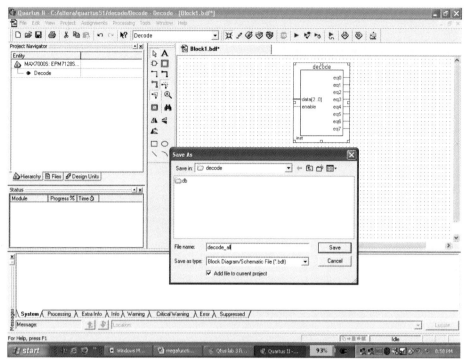

Figure 11

14. Once the Save As window is gone, right click on the symbol file and open up the options menu.

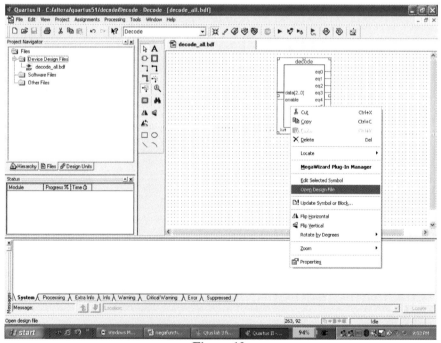

Figure 12

15. Before we open the Design File, notice in Figure 12 over on the left in the Project Navigator, I've clicked on the Files tab. It shows under the Device Design files our custom decoder: decoder_all.bdf. Check that yours shows the same thing.

16. Open Design File and select decode.vhd for the design file you wish to view. This is the Hardware Description Language script that is used to model the decoder. Slide down to view the actual coding. It's sometimes easier to write a description than draw in eight AND gates and wire them up to the correct inputs. You will learn about this language in a more advanced class. There are no gates in the design file as you've become accustomed to but just a text description of them and how they are connected.

```
    ENTITY decode IS
       PORT
       (
            data        : IN STD_LOGIC_VECTOR (2 DOWNTO 0);
            enable      : IN STD_LOGIC ;
            eq0     : OUT STD_LOGIC ;
            eq1     : OUT STD_LOGIC ;
            eq2     : OUT STD_LOGIC ;
            eq3     : OUT STD_LOGIC ;
            eq4     : OUT STD_LOGIC ;
            eq5     : OUT STD_LOGIC ;
            eq6     : OUT STD_LOGIC ;
            eq7     : OUT STD_LOGIC
       );
    END decode;


    ARCHITECTURE SYN OF decode IS

        SIGNAL sub_wire0    : STD_LOGIC_VECTOR (7 DOWNTO 0);
        SIGNAL sub_wire1    : STD_LOGIC ;
        SIGNAL sub_wire2    : STD_LOGIC ;
        SIGNAL sub_wire3    : STD_LOGIC ;
        SIGNAL sub_wire4    : STD_LOGIC ;
        SIGNAL sub_wire5    : STD_LOGIC ;
```

Figure 13

17. Close the open tab viewing the Design File decode.vhd. Let's get ready to simulate the design. You will need a 3 input waveform with an enable bit. If you bundle the enable input with the bus inputs, make the enable the MSB (most significant bit). Then you can simulate the design using four inputs and a count of 15. Or you could make it a separate input. In the last lab, we named the input bus nodes; for this lab, reverse the process.

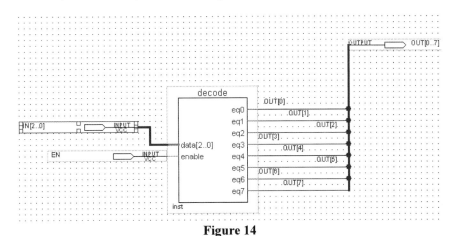

Figure 14

18. Except for the simulation and board testing, we're done. Now comes the big IF: compile the file (and save it). When you save the file, rename it "decode_all". Let's look at the first warning…

19. Elaborating entity "Decode"...fancy that. Let's see if we can fix the warning by going to Project and clicking on Add/Remove Files in Project...

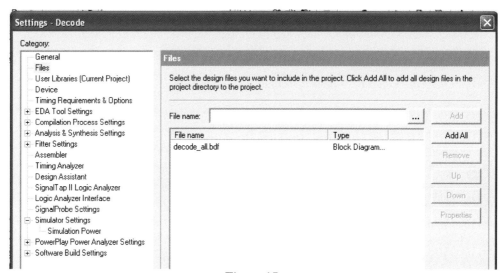

Figure 15

20. In the Setting-Decode popup box, click on the search button (the three dots "...") so we can find Decode.vhd. When you find it (it should be in the decode folder), click on Add and you'll notice that it joins the list below. We could rightly conclude that this box must list all the files in the project.

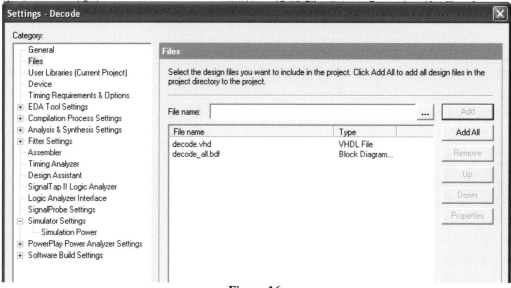

Figure 16

21. The second warning is inherent to this device family so we are not going to worry about it.

22. Next step is to simulate the design. You'll need a waveform. Select File, New, last tab...need a vwf. Search for the nodes...by right-clicking on Name and then selecting Insert Node or Bus...

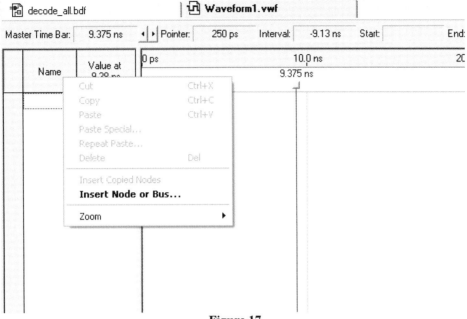

Figure 17

23. On that pop-up window, click on Node Finder...

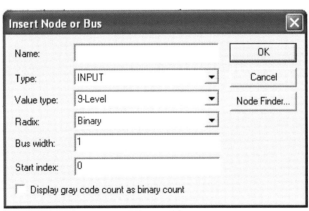

Figure 18

24. In the Node Finder, click on List, then move all the nodes from the Nodes Found box to the Nodes selected box by clicking on the >> button. Now click okay.

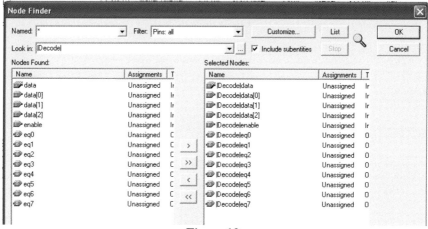

Figure 19

25. It looks like we didn't need the nodes data[0], data[1], and data[2] so just click on them and delete them. Click on data (the bus) so that the entire row is highlighted in addition to the name. Right click to open up the choices box and select Count Value.

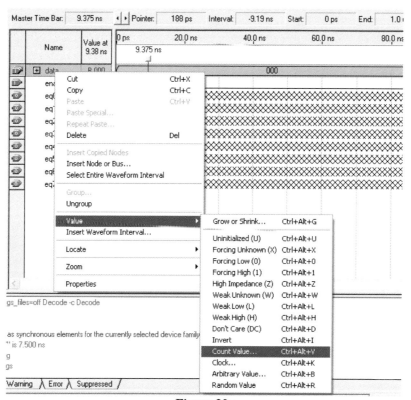

Figure 20

26. On the Count value pop-up box, most of the setting in the Counting tab are okay (radix = binary) because the project was compiled; however, I do like the Timing to be slightly slower. So click on the Timing tab and change the *Count every* 10 ns to 20 ns then click okay. Notice that the period for the simulation lasts from 0 ps to 1 μsecond.

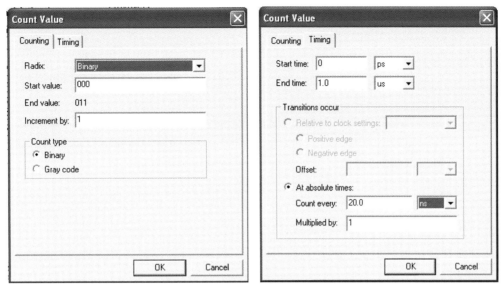

Figure 21

27. Click okay, save the waveform by some name you'll recognize. Make sure this is the assigned waveform for this project. Go to Assignments on the main menu, click on Settings, and then click on the Simulation Setting options. The waveform you've just created should appear in *Simulation input* that is presently blank as seen in Figure 21. If not, then browse for your file.

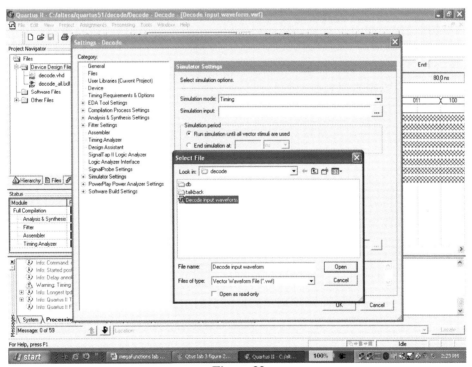

Figure 22

28. Now click on the Simulator button. Use Control+shift+space to back out to see the entire waveform. If there is no output, it might be because your enable input

is low. Force it high.

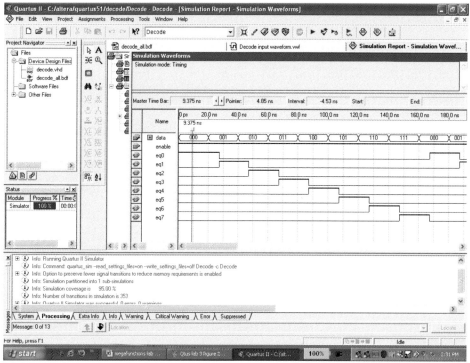

Figure 23

29. Looks good. When your input changes (increments by one) you select a different output. Each count value selects a different output. Imagine what you could do with that function; all controlled by incrementing bits on a bus. It's sequential, too.

30. A bit of troubleshooting. If you go back into the project at a later time and it doesn't open up the design, check to see that your graphics file decode_all.bsf is included in the project files. Also, try setting decode_all.bsf as the top-level file. The top-level file is at the top of the hierarchy so that it pops up when you select that project. To designate a file thusly, go to Assignments, Setting, General and browse to the desired file.

31. You're not done yet as you have to assign pins to the device and test it in the chip. You could insert inverters into the outputs so that when an output is selected, the LED lights; or just invert your logic for reading the LED's: An off output is lit and the selected output is off. Have the instructor check your evaluation board. Print out the design files, this successful simulation and a cover sheet.

56

Adders

Objective: To create and understand a half adder, full adder and a 4-bit adder. This lab tests student knowledge of Quartus procedures as it includes no Quartus specific directions.

Instructions:

1. First create and simulate the half adder in Figure 1.

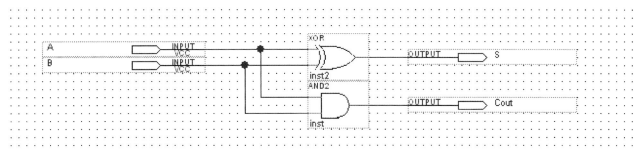

Figure 1 Half Adder

2. What is the truth table of the half-adder?

3. Simulate the design. What is the worse-case delay thru the half-adder?

4. As may see, the half adder is simple and fast, but has some draw backs. When adding numbers with multiple bits, the half adder is unable to handle carry-in bits. This problem can be resolved by using a full adder. Create and simulate the full adder shown in Figure 2.

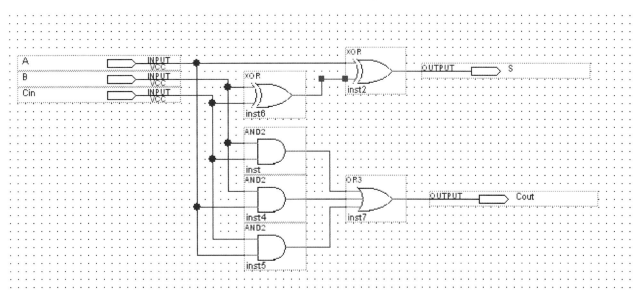

Figure 2 Full Adder

5. Simulate the full adder circuit and record the truth table.

6. What is the Boolean equation for the full adder?

7. What is the worse-case delay thru the full adder?

8. Create a full adder using two half-adders based upon the design seen on page 352 of your text (10th Ed.).

9. Which design is faster?

10. Create a symbol block for the full adder so that it can be used in the next part of the lab.

11. Create the 4 bit adder as shown in Figure 3. The circuit will add two four bit numbers together and give the 4 bit output. The Cout of the fourth full adder is the overflow output. This could be used for an input of another full adder or to be used as a fifth bit of the sum output.

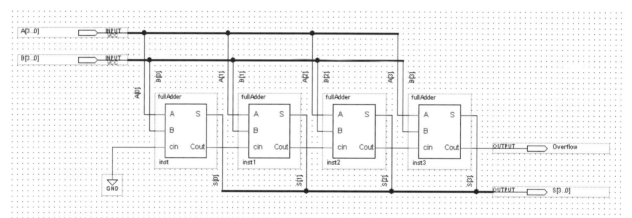

Figure 3 Four-bit Adder

12. Simulate the 4 bit adder. Record the output results.

13. What is the worse-case delay thru the 4-bit adder?

14. Drop your design into a UP-1 evaluation board and show your instructor the results. Please align the input bits MSB to LSB on the toggle switches so that they are arranged left to right.

Accumulator

Objective: To create and understand the operation of a 4-bit accumulator.

Instructions:

1. Create the accumulator circuit seen in Figure 1. Next program the circuit into the Altera board.

2. Use 7 dip switches: four for the data input, 1 switch for the Load, 1 switch for the Clear, and 1 switch for the Transfer. Use four of the onboard LED's for the output bits. You can connect the carry-out with output pin if you wish.

3. In order to use the accumulator, you must follow a set sequence for the control inputs.
    a. Toggle the Clear switch. This will clear the output register **B**. The LEDs will all turn on to indicate the data word: 0000. The Clear switch should be left in the HIGH position when not in use...otherwise you output will always read zero.
    b. Set the value of the input on the rocker switches.
    c. Toggle the Load switch which will clock the **A** register. Setting the Load switch to high and back will trigger the clocks of the D flip-flops making up the **A** register. This enters the input values into the flip-flops which pass them into the full adders.
    d. Toggle the Transfer switch. This will trigger the clocks of the four D flip-flops used as memory (register **B**) allowing the Sum to be sent back to the full adders and show the Sum on the output. If this is the first value entered, it will be seen on the output LEDs as the sum of the value plus zero.
    e. Change the rocker switches to represent the next data word.
    f. If this is an addition operation, toggle the Load switch to load the second value into the **A** register. The number that was occupying the register has all ready been passed to register **B**. If this is a multiplication operation, skip this step and go to instruction 3-j.
    g. When the Transfer switch is toggled a second time, the sum of the first two data words is displayed.
    h. If more than two numbers are to be added, begin again at instruction 3-b.
    i. To clear the memory flip-flops, simply toggle the Clear switch.
    j. If this is a multiplication, a second number is not loaded into the **A** register. Rather, the Transfer switch is operated the appropriate number of times to represent the value of the multiplier. You've all ready operated it once when you see the input value on the output.

4. Test basic functionality by loading a 0001 into the accumulator then transferring the data several times.   The output value should increment by one with each transfer. If the switch bounces, the output may change to unexpected values.

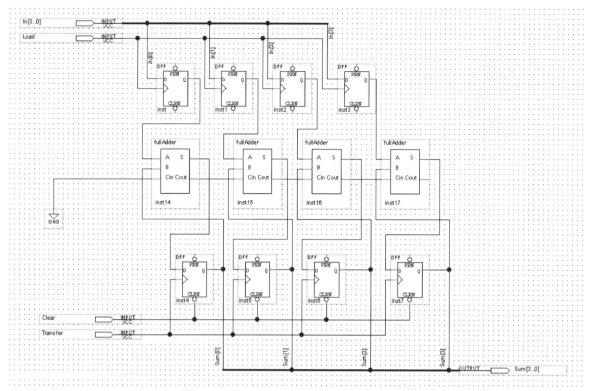

Figure 1 Simple accumulator

5. In the following table enter the following data and record the output.

Input	Operation	Outputs
	Clear	
0101	Load, Transfer	
0110	Add (Load, Transfer)	
	Clear	
0110	Load, Transfer	
0010	Multiply (x-fer 1 more time)	
	Clear	
0010	Load, Transfer	
0001	Add (Load, Transfer)	
1010	Add (Load, Transfer)	
	Clear	
0100	Load, Transfer	
0010	Add (Load, Transfer)	
0011	Multiply[1](…xfer 3 more times)	

6. In the last set, what number is being multiplied? What number were you expecting?

---

[1] If you have wired up the last Carry-out to an output pin and then to an LED, you may see this output operate.

Debounce

Objective: Students learn how to de-sensitize toggle switches and push buttons used on the Altera UP-1 board. Using an oscilloscope, students observe a phenomenon known as switch bounce. They determine the time period over which a logic circuit is susceptible to unintentional changes from analogue inputs. They compare three debounce circuit designs for reliability. Students make a selection of the best design, write up its performance characteristics, and save their design as a block symbol for use in I/O systems.

Instructions:
1. Connect an oscilloscope to the output of one of the toggle switches on the UP-1 board. Adjust the oscilloscope time base so that you can observe the transition of the DC power level when the toggle switch is activated. Capture some examples of switch bounce on the oscilloscope for inclusion on your lab report. See the appendix for instructions on how to do this on the new oscilloscopes.
2. Write down in your lab report sample time periods (and the frequency) of individual spikes. What is the longest time period you observe for all the spikes (considered as a group) to cease?
3. The follow signal is a sample of the switch bounce that this lab is designed to eliminate.

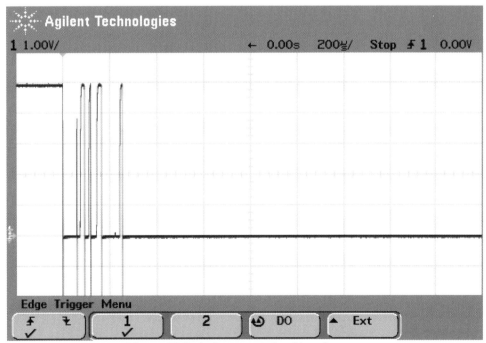

Figure 30 Switch generated voltage bounce.

4. Make the switch debounce seen in Figure 1 as our first test circuit. This design can be built in Quartus then dropped to the chip. The Input is wired to an I/O pin that is hooked up to our bouncy switch. The output is wired to any I/O pin and then connected to a 2nd oscilloscope lead. The clock is wired to PIN 83 Global Clock. The Global Clock is wired internally to the D flip-flop with that pin designation.

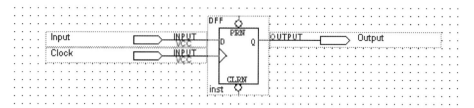

Figure 31 Simple debounce circuit

Test Sequence

5. Test this design and capture some of the oscilloscope dual displays for inclusion in your lab report.

6. Does this circuit effectively operate as a debounce for the switch? To determine this answer, conduct a trial: a testing sequence of 20 or 25 operations. What is the percentage of successful operations where there was bounce on the input but none on the output? To correctly answer this question, do not include as part of the count those operations of the switch where there was no detectable bounce on the input. Include your test results in the lab report.

7. What would be the reason(s) for failure of this debounce circuit to operate as expected? To answer this question, compare your inputs to the AND gate, flip-flop delay time, and the clock frequency. Include your reasoning in a written paragraph in your lab report for this debounce design.

8. Redesign your test circuit so that the input clock of the flip-flop is connected to an ordinary input pin.

9. Conduct the Test Sequence described in step 5 again on this debounce circuit with the following modifications:
   a. Connect an external function generation set on a square wave (amplitude set to not exceed the Altera chip input specifications…5 volts)
   b. Test at two different frequencies:
      i. One twice as fast as the time for the longest group delay determined in step 2
      ii. The 2nd would be twice as long as the longest group delays.
   c. Include these test results in your lab report. In your opinion, which was the better design?

10. We're now going to design a different type of switch debounce that utilizes a shift register and an AND gate to verify the termination of any bounce. Part of the design will allow us to generate an acceptable clock frequency from the global clock by using a technique called frequency division.

11. Open up a project called debounce and begin this design by adding a part called lpm_counter to make a frequency divider.

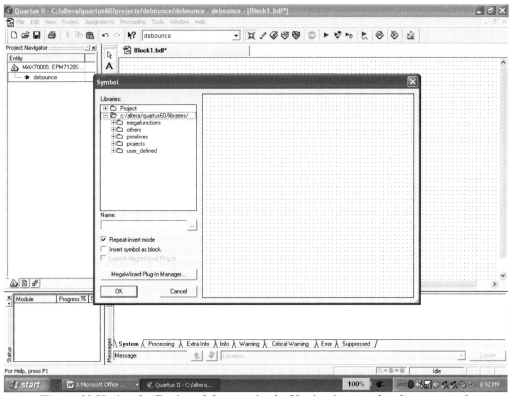

Figure 32 Notice the Project debounce in the Navigation tree has been created.

12. The part is found by clicking on the MegaWizard Plug-In Manager button then finding lpm_counter under arithmetic in the Megafunction folder. Check Figure 3 for the path.

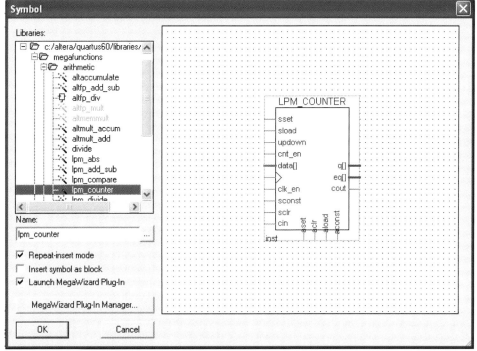

Figure 33 Use MegaWizard Plug-In Manager to insert a counter into your design.

13. Choices you should make in the creation of the counter (the simpler the better) is an output bus 32 bits wide and no additional ports for the next two screens, click past the included files then click finish. After this is dropped onto your schematic file, add an input I/O port for the clock which you will wire to the Global Clock by assign the input to pin 83. Also, when the file was compiled, Quartus gave a warning that the design file for this circuit was not included. This can be circumvented by adding lpm_counter0.vhd to the design via Assignments>Files.

⚠ Warning: Timing Analysis does not support the analysis of latches as synchronous elements for the currently
⊞ ⚠ Warning: Found pins functioning as undefined clocks and/or memory enables
⊞ ⚠ Warning: Found 1 node(s) in clock paths which may be acting as ripple and/or gated clocks -- node(s) analyz

Figure 34 Only warnings showing when file is compiled.

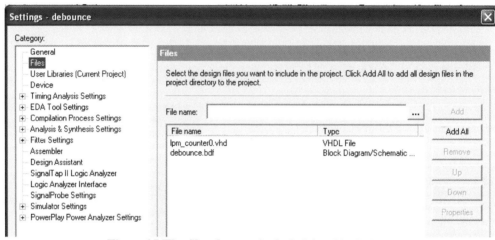

Figure 35 The files that are included for this design.

14. Add four D flip-flops to the design. Wire them up so the output of one goes to the input of the next. The first D flip-flop input should be called data_in and assigned to an available I/O pin on the chip. Connect the toggle switch we are debouncing to this pin.

15. Insert a four input AND gate into the design. Connect the outputs of the four D flip-flops to the inputs of the AND gate. Connect the output of the AND gate to an available I/O pin. Connect the 2nd oscilloscope lead to this output.

16. The next portion of the design requires some calculation and this essential information is to be recorded in your lab report as Frequency Divider Calculations. The global clock will have to be divided X number of times by two to match the function generator frequency you evaluated as satisfactory in your second design. The number of times is the bit number because this is an up counter and the most significant bit is the slowest changing. Show your calculations.

17. On the design, connect the four clock inputs of the flip-flops together and draw a pseudo connection between the output of the counter and the clocks of the flip-flops. Assign the bit for this connection by labeling this section of wire q[xx]. The value of the xx should be equal to or greater than the division by two of the chip frequency you calculated previously. To assign the bit, click on the wire to select it then right click to select properties then you enter the label. Your completed circuit should look something like Figure 4. You may or may not be using bit 31

(the lowest available frequency) for your design. When the project compiled, it would not recognize a source for q[31] until I drew (and labeled q[31..0]) a stub bus on the lpm counter output.

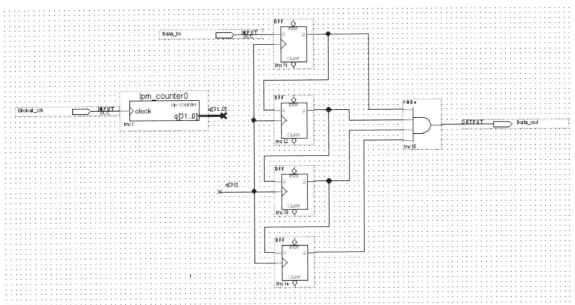

Figure 36 Debounce circuit with clock divider

18. The simulation of the design (seen below) reveals some design considerations.

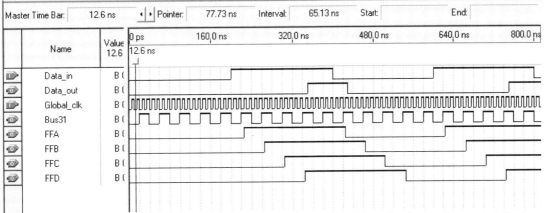

Figure 37 Simulation (with outputs of flip-flops revealed) showing delay of pulse on the output that significantly changes the duty cycle.

19. The clock speed of the flip-flops will affect the length of the output pulse. The principle revealed is the debounce has to be set so that the percentage of delay waiting for the pulses to settle should be small in comparison to the data pulse otherwise the pulse width is affected. Normally, the debounce design is used on asynchronous inputs (inputs from the real world). They usually are of long duration (i.e. setting of an option, coin depressing a switch) in comparison with the pulses.

20. Repeat the test sequence of Step 5 to verify the debounce circuit works as advertised and include the oscilloscope screen shots with the trial percent calculations.

21. Demonstrate your successful design for the instructor. Save the design as intellectual property for use in other designs with analogue inputs that could be subject to switch bounce by creating and saving a block symbol of your design. Include in your lab report screen shots of your three designs and the block symbol.

22. It is sometimes helpful to test your design via stages. To verify that you have the oscilloscope working correctly, insert an output pin off the input pin of the D flip-flop. The output of the lpm_counter can be checked by inserting an output pin on the q[31] bit wire. The period of this bit is 20 milliseconds so if you are looking to verify a working counter you will have to change the time division on the oscilloscope to a value a bit shorter. You could also check the outputs of the flip-flops by adding I/O pins to their outputs.

23. Students should submit their data collected with their analysis of the lab results and any other observations. Besides the circuit design, screen shots of the oscilloscope if possible should be included in their report. A comparison between the before (upper trace) and after (lower trace) of a debounce circuit is seen below.

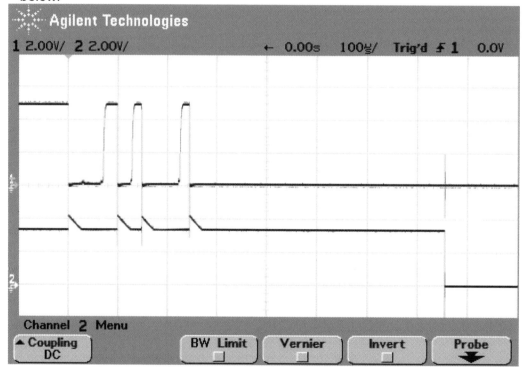

Figure 38 Before and after results for a debounce circuit.

24. This view shows three bounce spikes that are smoothed out by the debounce circuit. Because there are four flip-flops that have to read ones before turning on the output, there is a clocking delay thru the circuit. The faint pulses seen in the figure are due to the common grounds of the oscilloscope leads. Also, the output from the 4 input AND gate is normally held at 3.3 voltages. The peak (4.3 volts) seen when the input voltage falls to ground potential linearly fall off to the normal level over a short period. This peak also could be attributed to the common grounds of the oscilloscope leads. The output of the Altera chip is nominally 3.3 volts.

Adding a Digital Readout

Objective: Students create a schematic file that adds a digital readout to another designs. This lab assumes the design for a digital readout is being added to another design that has a binary 4-bit output.

Instructions:
1. Open the New Project Wizard and create the directory for this project.

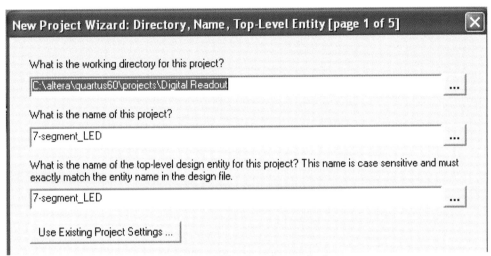

Figure 1 Naming the project

2. Once the project is established, click on File→New→ Block Diagram/Schematic File to begin entering the design on the virtual breadboard.
3. Find the 7448 (or the 7447 chip) in the parts library under *others/maxplus2* and add that to the board.

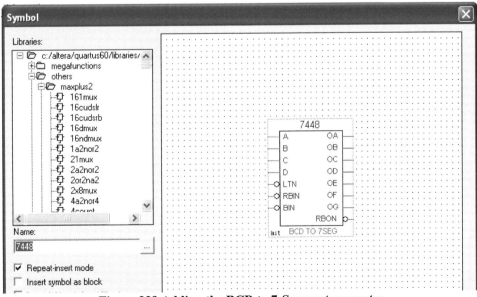

Figure 239 Adding the BCD to 7-Segment converter

4. Add seven output pins to OA thru OG. Right click on the output ports and change the name to the segment that it serves. In order to assign the ports to I/O pins we have to compile the project even though it appears incomplete at this stage.

5. Label the output pins with the appropriate I/O assignment as per the *7-Segment Display LED Pinouts* table information found in the reference section in the back. If you've forgotten how to assign pins, review the information in section *Place & Route* of Lab 1 on page 18 of this book.

6. Check that the I/O pin assigned shows up on the schematic. You're finished with the design of the Digital Readout. However, take a look at the insides of the 7448 by selecting it then right click to Open Design File. Since the 7-segment display is a common anode, to turn on a segment, the true condition has to be a low; thus, you should insert inverters in line with the outputs.

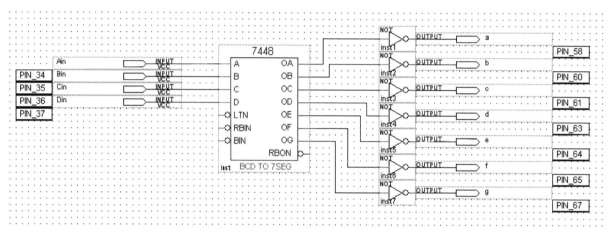

Figure 3 BCD to 7-segment LED

7. Test your design by adding the file *7-segment_LED.bdf* to one of your earlier projects; such as, the 4-bit adder. The input side of the design would be added at that time by naming the wires on the inputs according to the naming scheme of the outputs from the 4-bit adder.

8. Demonstrate the successful addition of this feature in another design such as the 4-bit adder or the accumulator to your instructor and submit the schematic drawing for *7-segment_LED.bdf* and the modified design for the test circuit.

Digital Logic Basics

Binary Conversion Table

Binary 4-bits	Decimal	Hexadecimal
0000	0	0
0001	1	1
0010	2	2
0011	3	3
0100	4	4
0101	5	5
0110	6	6
0111	7	7
1000	8	8
1001	9	9
1010	10	A
1011	11	B
1100	12	C
1101	13	D
1110	14	D
1111	15	F
0001 0000	16	10

Explanation of Number Base Formatting

Numbering systems have a base number that is considered the maximum number that can be counted before the system increments to the next column and resets. An example of this feature in the decimal number system whose largest number is 9 (but consists of ten digits) would be: 8, 9, 10. The second column (which just suddenly appears) is considered understood to be zero until it contains information other than zero. The same ideas apply to the binary numbering system and hexadecimal numbering system commonly used in digital logic. Technically, the value for each column is base raised to a power equal to the column number multiplied by the place holder. The value of a multiple column number is the sum of the values of each column. The first column (located in the right-most position of a number) is consider column 0, the second column (from the right) is column 1 and the hundreds position (the third column) is column 2. Thus a decimal number, such as, 126, can be evaluated as follows: $1*10^2+2*10^1+6*10^0 = 100+20+6 = 126$. Any number base raised to zero in the first column is by exponential rules equal to 1, thus the first column is always the unit column. In the binary system, the calculations are even easier because you can ignore any column whose placeholder is zero. For example: $10010= 1*2^4+0*2^3+0*2^2+1*2^1+0*2^0 = 16+0+0+2+0 = 16+2 = 18$. Experience digital designers jump immediately to the last evaluation shown before the sum because they have the 2's power table memorized.

The hexadecimal system is considered an alphanumerical system because of the use of letters after the 10th number, the evaluation is the same with the use of 16 for base. Digital circuits (computers) do not actually use the hexadecimal system in their circuits. Circuits are either on (1) or off (0). The base 16 numbering system is a display technique for the convenience for the human whose visual skills are not adapt at detecting differences in 16 (or greater) columns of numbers whose only digits consist of series of zeros and ones. When letters and 0-9 are inserted, we do much better.

Powers of Two

0	1	2	3	4	5	6	7	8
1	2	4	8	16	32	63	128	256

9	10	11	12	13	14	15	16
512	1024	2048	4096	8192	16384	32768	65536

Boolean Theorems

Digital circuits are made up of AND ($\cdot$) , OR (+), and NOT (negation bar) gates.

#	Theorem	Comments
1	$X \cdot 0 = 0$	A zero (gnd or off) turns off an AND output
2	$X \cdot 1 = X$	A one (power or on) enables the AND output
3	$X \cdot X = X$	An input AND with itself equals itself
4	$X \cdot \overline{X} = 0$	An input AND its negative turns off the output
5	$X + 0 = X$	An OR gate OR'ed with gnd enables the output
6	$X + 1 = 1$	An OR fate OR'ed with a one turns off the output
7	$X + X = X$	An input OR'ed with itself equals itself
8	$X \cdot \overline{X} = 1$	An input OR'ed its negative turns off the output
9	$X + Y = Y + X$	Inputs can be connected in any order, output will be the same
10	$X \cdot Y = Y \cdot X$	Inputs can be connected in any order, output will be the same
11	$(X + Y) + Z = (Y + X) + Z = X + Y + Z$	A two-input OR gate connected to a second two-input OR gate is the same as a three-input OR gate
12	$X \cdot (Y \cdot Z) = (Y \cdot X) \cdot Y = X \cdot Y \cdot Z$	A two-input AND gate connected to a second two-input AND gate is the same as a three-input AND gate
13a	$X \cdot (Y+Z) = X \cdot Y + X \cdot Z$	Same distribution rules as regular algebra
13b	$(W+X) \cdot (Y+Z) = W \cdot Y + X \cdot Y + W \cdot Z + X \cdot Z$	Same distribution rules as regular algebra
14	$X + X \cdot Y = X$	Input elimination rule
15a	$X + \overline{X} \cdot Y = X + Y$	1st gate elimination rule
15b	$\overline{X} + X \cdot Y = \overline{X} + Y$	2nd gate elimination rule
16	$\overline{(X + Y)} = \overline{X} * \overline{Y}$	DeMorgan Gate Rule: if you break the bar—change the sign
17	$\overline{(X * Y)} = \overline{X} + \overline{Y}$	DeMorgan Gate Rule: if you break the bar—change the sign

Reverse Logic

Theorems 1-4 off is a gnd (0) and enable (1) will pass the value of the X input thru to the output.

Theorems 5-8 off is a high (1) and enable (0) will pass the value of the X input thru to the output.

70

Websites for help on Boolean Theorems

Short and to the point summary: http://hyperphysics.phy-astr.gsu.edu/hbase/electronic/diglog.html
The same material covering digital logic with explanations:
http://www.eelab.usyd.edu.au/digital_tutorial/chapter4/4_0.html
A little more detailed workup: http://www.ecs.umass.edu/ece/engin112/lectures/Engin112-04-09-20.pdf
Another good explanation: http://www.allaboutcircuits.com/vol_4/chpt_7/1.html
The following site provides you with free software to solve Boolean equations. Highly recommended. http://www.puz.com/sw/karnaugh/index.htm

Combinational Logic Design Procedure

Step 1 Set up at truth table for the design.
Step 2 Write the AND term for each true output condition.
Step 3 Write the Sum-of-Products expression for the output.
Step 4 Simplify the output expression.
Step 5 Implement the expression in digital logic.

Steps 2 thru 4 can alternately be completed using a K-mapping technique.

State Machine Design Procedure

Transition Table Rules

Output transition	J input	K input
$0 \rightarrow 0$	0	X
$0 \rightarrow 1$	1	X
$1 \rightarrow 0$	X	1
$1 \rightarrow 1$	X	0

Step 1 Determine the number of bits (FFs) and the desired counting sequence.
Step 2 Draw the State Diagram showing all possible states.
Step 3 Set up the Present State/Next State transition table.
    Present State is the ordinary counting sequence.
    Next State is the state the machine transitions to next determined by the State Diagram.
Step 4 Complete the Present State/Next State transition table for each J & K input per FF using the Transition Table Rules seen above.
Step 5 Using the steps from Combinational Logic Design Procedure in the previous section, determine the input logic to each J and K for each FF. A blank template for calculating a State Machine of MOD 8 is provided on the next page.
Step 6 Implement the design.

Present State				Next State				Jc	Kc	Jb	Kb	Ja	Ka
C	B	A		C	B	A							
0	0	0											
0	0	1											
0	1	0											
0	1	1											
1	0	0											
1	0	1											
1	1	0											
1	1	1											

C	B	A	Jc
0	0	0	
0	0	1	
0	1	0	
0	1	1	
1	0	0	
1	0	1	
1	1	0	
1	1	1	

	nA	A
nC nB		
nC B		
C B		
C nB		

C	B	A	Kc
0	0	0	
0	0	1	
0	1	0	
0	1	1	
1	0	0	
1	0	1	
1	1	0	
1	1	1	

	nA	A
nC nB		
nC B		
C B		
C nB		

C	B	A	Jb
0	0	0	
0	0	1	
0	1	0	
0	1	1	
1	0	0	
1	0	1	
1	1	0	
1	1	1	

	nA	A
nC nB		
nC B		
C B		
C nB		

C	B	A	Kb
0	0	0	
0	0	1	
0	1	0	
0	1	1	
1	0	0	
1	0	1	
1	1	0	
1	1	1	

	nA	A
nC nB		
nC B		
C B		
C nB		

C	B	A	Ja
0	0	0	
0	0	1	
0	1	0	
0	1	1	
1	0	0	
1	0	1	
1	1	0	
1	1	1	

	nA	A
nC nB		
nC B		
C B		
C nB		

C	B	A	Ka
0	0	0	
0	0	1	
0	1	0	
0	1	1	
1	0	0	
1	0	1	
1	1	0	
1	1	1	

	nA	A
nC nB		
nC B		
C B		
C nB		

Appendix

7-Segment Display LED Pinouts

Display Segment	Pins for Digit 1	Pins for Digit 2
A	58	69
B	60	70
C	61	73
D	63	74
E	64	76
F	65	75
G	67	77
Decimal Point	68	79

The segments for the two 7-segment display LEDs are directly wired to the above I/O output pins. In any design using the evaluation board that incorporates a 7-segment display output, once you assign the pin for a particular segment, you do not need to place a jumper; in fact, there is no place to connect the far end of the jumper. The jumpers are embedded in the board design connecting that pin with the input to the LED segment. The segment turns on by driving the output I/O pin low.

Technically, the I/O pins are available for assignment for other purposes but be advised that you have double terminated the output. A double termination can cause some projects to appear not to operate correctly. You'll notice that the segment that is double terminated may turn on when the I/O pin is active; a low is present on the pin. The resistance of the LED segment is in parallel with the path for the alternate use. If the alternate use is significantly lower in resistance that the LED segment then no effect may be seen. If the alternate use is of similar resistance value, then the current divides and this may cause an apparent malfunction of the alternate use.

LED Connections and Logic

The UP Education Boards contain 16 LEDs that are pulled-up with a 330-Ω resistor. An LED is illuminated when a logic 0 is applied to the female header associated with the LED. LEDs D1 through D8 are connected in the same sequence to the female headers (i.e., D1 is connected to position 1, and D2 is connected to position 2, etc.). LEDs D9 through D16 are connected in the same sequence to the female headers (i.e., D9 is connected to position 1, and D10 is connected to position 2, etc.). See Figure 3.

Figure 3. LED Positions

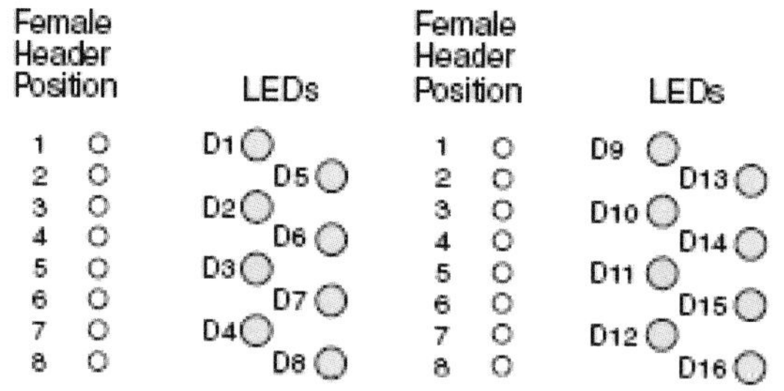

EPM7128S Device

The UP1 and UP2 Education Boards provide the following resources for the EPM7128S device.

- Socket-mounted 84-pin PLCC package
- Signal pins that are accessible via female headers
- JTAG chain connection for the ByteBlasterMV cable
- Two momentary push-button switches
- Two octal dual inline package (DIP) switches
- 16 LEDs
- Dual-digit seven-segment display
- On-board oscillator (25.175 MHz)

74

UP-1 Evaluation Board Pinouts

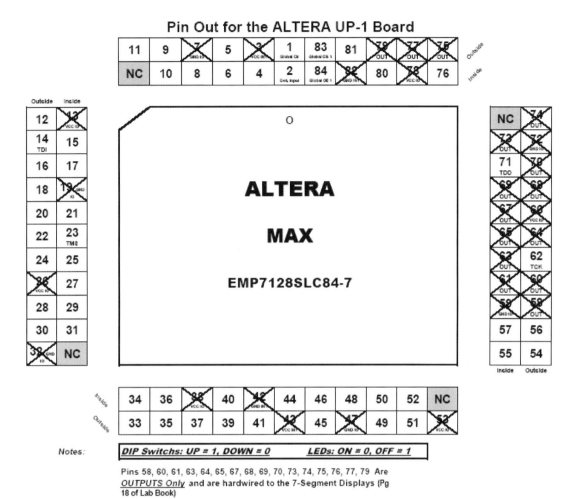

Pin Out for the ALTERA UP-1 Board

DIP Switchs: UP = 1, DOWN = 0   LEDs: ON = 0, OFF = 1

Pins 58, 60, 61, 63, 64, 65, 67, 68, 69, 70, 73, 74, 75, 76, 77, 79 Are
OUTPUTS Only and are hardwired to the 7-Segment Displays (Pg
18 of Lab Book)

I/O crossed out are not used for ordinary input and output functions.
Contributed by Joe Diecidue

Toggle Switch Logic

MAX_PB1 & MAX_PB2 Push-Buttons

MAX_PB1 and MAX_PB2 are two push-buttons that provide active-low signals and are pulled-up through 10-KΩ resistors. Connections to these signals are easily made by inserting one end of the hook-up wire into the push-button female header. The other end of the hook-up wire should be inserted into the appropriate female header assigned to the I/O pin of the EPM7128S device.

MAX_SW1 & MAX_SW2 Switches

MAX_SW1 and MAX_SW2 each contain eight switches that provide logic-level signals. These switches are pulled-up through 10-KΩ resistors. Connections to these signals are made by inserting one end of the hook-up wire into the female header aligned with the appropriate switch. Insert the other end of the hook-up wire into the appropriate female header assigned to the I/O pin of the EPM7128S device. The switch output is set to logic 1 when the switch is open and set to logic 0 when the switch is closed.

I/O Pin Voltage Levels

MAX 7000 device outputs can be programmed to meet a variety of system-level requirements.

MultiVolt I/O Interface

MAX 7000 devices—except 44-pin devices—support the MultiVolt I/O interface feature, which allows MAX 7000 devices to interface with systems that have differing supply voltages. The 5.0-V devices in all packages can be set for 3.3-V or 5.0-V I/O pin operation. These devices have one set of VCC pins for internal operation and input buffers (VCCINT), and another set for I/O output drivers (VCCIO).

The VCCINT pins must always be connected to a 5.0-V power supply. With a 5.0-V V_{CCINT} level, input voltage thresholds are at TTL levels, and are therefore compatible with both 3.3-V and 5.0-V inputs.

The VCCIO pins can be connected to either a 3.3-V or a 5.0-V power supply, depending on the output requirements. When the VCCIO pins are connected to a 5.0-V supply, the output levels are compatible with 5.0-V systems. When V_{CCIO} is connected to a 3.3-V supply, the output high is 3.3 V and is therefore compatible with 3.3-V or 5.0-V systems. Devices operating with V_{CCIO} levels lower than 4.75 V incur a nominally greater timing delay of t_{OD2} instead of t_{OD1}.

Open-Drain Output Option (MAX 7000S Devices Only)

MAX 7000S devices provide an optional open-drain (functionally equivalent to open-collector) output for each I/O pin. This open-drain output enables the device to provide system-level control signals (e.g., interrupt and write enable signals) that can be asserted by any of several devices. It can also provide an additional wired-OR plane.

On-Board Voltage Regulator

The on-board voltage regulator, an LM340T, regulates the DC positive input at 5 V. The DC input consists of two holes for connecting a 5-V DC regulated power source. The hole marked with a plus sign (+) is the positive input; the hole marked with a minus sign (–) is board common. A green light-emitting diode (LED) labeled POWER is illuminated when current is flowing from the 5-V DC-regulated power source.

How to capture switch bounce on the Agilent 54622D 100MHz Oscilloscope

1. Connect a scope lead from the #1 scope BNC input to one of the pushbutton switches on the UP-1 board. Connect the positive lead (red) to the pin for the pushbutton and the negative lead to the negative pin for the voltage regulator. Turn on the scope.
2. Press:
   a. the *Save/Recall* button in the File area of the front panel.
   b. the *Default Setup* soft key on the screen menu.
   c. the *Main/Delayed* button found in the Horizontal portion of the front panel.
   d. the *Time Ref Center* soft key on the screen menu until it reads *Time Ref Left*.
   e. the *Mode /Coupling* button found in the Trigger portion of the front panel.
   f. the *Mode Auto* soft key and set it to *Normal*.
3. The amplitude of the signal is expected to be 5 volts so set the voltage display to 1 or 2 volts per division. Move the ground as need to display the full value transition.
4. Press the *Single* button found under the Run Control portion of the front panel. Now press the Altera UP-1 pushbutton under test and one transition will be captured turning the *Run/Stop* button red. To clear the display and capture another sample, press the *Single* button followed by the UP-1 button.
5. The captured transition can then be expanded using the horizontal time base knob to view any bounce condition captured in the display. By changing the transition edge on the soft menu, you can capture rising and falling edge bounce. Figure 1 is a sample of switch bounce.
6. If you wish to utilize the dual trace capability of the oscilloscope, simple turn on the #2 input by pressing the #2 button on the front panel and adjust the ground plus the volts per division for viewing clarity.
7. A copy of the oscilloscope screen can be placed into a Word document by enabling the Agilent Intuilink software toolbar on the Word menu. A shortcut has been placed on the desktop on all the college's computers in the Electronic labs at Wentworth Institute of Technology. After enabling the toolbar, click on the camera icon to copy the scope's visual display in a document.

Printed in the United States
86012LV00001BF